Where
Does
Everyone
Go?

Where Does Everyone Go?

by AILEEN FISHER

illustrated by Adrienne Adams

THOMAS Y. CROWELL COMPANY

NEW YORK

By Aileen Fisher

GOING BAREFOOT

WHERE DOES EVERYONE GO?

LIKE NOTHING AT ALL

I LIKE WEATHER

LISTEN, RABBIT

IN THE MIDDLE OF THE NIGHT

ARBOR DAY

BEST LITTLE HOUSE

THE VALLEY OF THE SMALLEST

TO
ADRIENNE

What happens to everyone
in the Fall
when the days get short
and the sun gets small
and leaves go skidding
on every breeze
and apples are picked
from the apple trees
and at night the edges
of puddles freeze?

What happens to everyone?

Anyone know?

Where in the Fall
does everyone *go*?

I know about birds
like wrens and swallows:
one flies off
and another follows
over the hills
and fields and hollows.
They fly away
from the frosts of Winter.
(Do they get their maps
from a Bird-Map printer?)

But where in the Fall
do other things go?
Do you know?

I went looking
up and down
for a bug, sort of reddish
and orangy-brown,
with spots on its back
like dots on a clown.

But there wasn't a ladybug
left in town!

I poked under leaves
in ditches.
I peered into holes
and niches.
I peeked under clumps
of clover.
I turned humps of leaf-mold
over.
I looked under stones
where the ground was bare,
but there wasn't a ladybug
anywhere.

Where did they go?

I asked Aunt Jo.
I asked my mother.
I asked one neighbor
after another . . .
and now I know.

Before the summery
weather ends
ladybugs fly
to meet their friends
and get in touch
with cousins and such.

On a woodsy mountain
or far-off hill
they visit together
until the weather
turns gray and chill,

And then they crowd
into cracks and creases
and yawn, and cuddle,
and sleep their fill
till Winter gradually
falls to pieces
and days get warm
and the wind is still.

That's why, when hills
turn buff and brown,
there aren't any ladybugs
left in town.

What happens to everyone
when it's cool
and leaf-boats sink
on the black-eyed pool
and brothers and sisters
stay late at school,
and wearing a sweater's
a very good rule?

Where does everyone go?

I went looking
high and low
around the yard
and the patio
for something that flitted there
weeks ago.

Where were the fluttery butterflies
that used to rise
and glide on the breeze?

Not in the trees.
Not in the sky.

Not in the bushes
low and high.

Where did they go?

I asked my mother.
I asked Aunt Jo.
I asked one neighbor
and then another . . .
so now I know!

It's rather sad
but I guess it's true:
most of the butterflies' lives
are through
when Summer is old
and Autumn's new . . .
they don't keep living
like me and you.

Most of the butterflies
freeze to a splinter
at the glint
at the squint
at the *hint* of Winter.
They've laid their eggs
and their lives are over.
Their frail wings fall
to the grass and clover.

But that's not the case
with the Monarchs, though.
They fly to a place
too sunny for snow . . .

They gather in flocks,
they gather in crowds,
they sail over rocks,
they glide under clouds,
they float over ridges
and cities and bridges
south, south
to Butterfly Trees
where they take their ease
away from the blizzards
that make us freeze
and sniffle
and sneeze.

That's the reason
when Fall's in season
you seldom see butterflies
flitting
or sitting.

What happens to everyone
when it's colder
and days are darker
and getting older,
and a tired-out sun
looks over your shoulder?

Where in the Fall
does everyone *go*?

I went walking
back and forth
to the west and east
and south and north,
to the cattail pond
and the marsh beyond
where turtles and frogs
used to sit around
on moss-covered logs
on moss-covered ground.

But there weren't any frogs
or warty toads.

There weren't any turtles
or peepers or lizards.
They'd vanished like wizards!

Where did they *go*?

They couldn't fly off like swallows
over the hills and hollows,
like ladybugs by dozens
going to meet their cousins,
like Monarchs gliding quickly
before the snow got tickly.

Where did they go?

I asked my mother.
I asked Aunt Jo
and all the neighbors.
So now I know!

When days get breezy
and nights get freezy
frogs sink down
in the mud and ooze
for a good long snooze.

It isn't a very clean bed
to choose
(I'm glad it isn't
the kind *I* use)
but frogs aren't queasy
and sleeping is easy
down where it's warm
away from the storm.

They're sound asleep
during all the blizzards,
and so are toads
under rocks, and lizards.

That's why you never
see frogs at all—
bullfrogs big
or peepers small—
or hopperty toads
when it's half-past Fall.

Where's everyone
now that the meadow
is cold
in the autumn shadow?
Where are the furry ones,
scamper-and-scurry ones,
in-a-great-hurry ones?

Where are the chippies,
the woodchucks, the bears?
Are they all busy
with autumn affairs,
putting on storm doors
and making repairs?

Where are the badgers,
the bats, and the skunks?
Working on bed socks
and quilts for their bunks?

Do you know?

I looked all over.
I looked all day.
I looked for woodchucks
where woodchucks stay.
I looked for furries
(both up and down)
plain, and with stripes
of white and brown.

But there weren't any chippies
and such in town!

Where did they *go*?

I asked Aunt Jo
and Everyone Else.
So now I know:

Woodchucks and chippies,
skunks and bears
(now that it's Fall)
are snug in their lairs,
snug in their dens
near roots of trees,
curled with their noses
between their knees,
away from the cold
and the biting breeze.

They'll sleep
in a heap
till Winter is over
and there's gold in the sun
and green in the clover.

That's why you only see deer
and mice
and maybe a weasel once or twice,
when Winter is here,
and leap-away rabbits
and squirrels
who haven't such sleep-away habits.

Where's everyone after school
today when the sky
is gray and cool
and all the windows of trees
are bare
without any curtains of leaves
up there?

The street is a noisy one
as a rule
but now it's quiet
when I walk by,
quiet as clouds
in the cloudy sky.

I wonder why.

Where, I wonder,
did everyone go?

There's my brother . . .
he ought to know.

"If it starts to rain
it may turn to snow!"
my brother shouts,
with his face aglow.

"Everyone's off
in a hustle and bustle
to tussle with skis
in need of wax
and skates to be sharpened
and sleds to make tracks!

"Everyone's digging
for winter rigging,"
my brother shouts
and his feet start jigging.

"We have to get ready
for winter weather,
for flakes coming down
as big as a feather,"
my brother says
as we run together.

Oh, but I'm glad
I'm not a chippy
who goes to sleep
when the nights get nippy
and days get zippy.

Oh, but I'm glad
I'm not a lizard
or beetle or bear
who misses a blizzard
from A to izzard.

Think of sleeping
the Winter through
or going south
for a summer view
when it's starting to do
what it's starting to do . . .

It's starting to rain!

And everyone knows
at this time of year
when a storm–cloud shows
it oftentimes snows.

It's starting to rain . . .
and what do you know?
It really,
it really
is turning to snow!

We'll go to the park
and have a lark
in the snow before dark!

We'll climb to the crown
of the hill near town
and ride our sleds down!

We'll glide on our skis
past snow-flower trees
and whizz through the breeze!

Hi-ho, hi-ho,
just look at it snow . . .
with Everyone full
of a place to go.

ABOUT THE AUTHOR

Aileen Fisher was five years old when her family
moved to a farm near the small town
of Iron River, Michigan.
There she learned to know many different kinds
of animals and birds—from horses and chickens to
chipmunks and rabbits.
She enjoyed the changing seasons and the four-mile walk
each day back and forth to school.
Her first poetry appeared in the high-school column
of the town newspaper.
Since then she has written a number
of books for children.
After graduating from the University of Missouri,
Miss Fisher worked in Chicago
for a few years. Later she moved to
a 200-acre ranch in the foothills of Colorado.
It is in this setting that she writes her
stories and poems.

ABOUT THE ILLUSTRATOR

Adrienne Adams attended Stephens College and
the University of Missouri. Soon afterward she entered
the art field and became a display art director
and a free-lance designer.
Her first illustrating was done for
a book written by her husband. She has since devoted all
her time to illustrating children's books.
Miss Adams lives and works
in a stone and log home on twenty-one acres
of land in New Jersey.
Her winters are spent in the Virgin Islands,
where she has a small house overlooking Cruz Bay.